Young Learner's

My Favourite Stories

The Cat and the Rooster
Haku's Power

C000299110

The Cat and the Rooster

Once upon a time there was a cat and a rooster who were good friends. They lived together in the same house. The cat played the fiddle well and the rooster sang lovely songs.

The cat went out every morning to gather food for the two of them. The rooster stayed indoors in the safety of the house.

A fox had been wanting to eat the rooster for dinner. One day after the cat had left, the fox called out to the rooster, "I have brought some tasty grains for you. Come out and eat!"

The rooster knew that the fox was clever and wanted to eat him. He locked the door quickly so that the fox could not enter the house.

The cunning fox spread out some wheat grains on the ground and hid in the bushes. The rooster looked out of the window and saw the tasty grains. He looked all around and saw no one. "Good!" he thought to himself, "The fox has left. I can go out and eat the grains quickly."

As he began to peck at the grains the fox leapt out of the bushes and caught him.
As the fox carried the rooster away, he sang,
"Save me, brother Puss I pray!
Fox is taking me far away
If you don't come soon my friend
I shall surely meet my end."

In the evening, the cat returned and found the rooster missing. As he went out looking for him, a rabbit told the cat about the fox. The cat was very angry! He took his fiddle and a sack and went to the fox's house. The fox was busy boiling a pot of water to cook the rooster. Her four children were playing outside.

The cat began playing the fiddle. The children heard the fiddle and happily went and sat beside the cat. The cat quickly caught them and put them in the sack.

Then the cat called out, "Listen fox, I have your children with me! If you want them back, set my rooster friend free right now."
The fox ran out of her house and begged, "Please don't harm my children. I shall never trouble you or the rooster ever again."

Saying so, she freed the rooster. The cat also let the fox's children out of the sack.
The fox was happy to have her children back. The cat and the rooster hugged each other and went back home.

Moral: A friend in need is a friend indeed.

Haku's Power

Haku was a hard-working stonecutter. One day, as he was busy cutting a huge stone, he saw the king and his royal procession passing by.

Looking at the king, the stonecutter thought, "I work so hard all day, yet I live the life of a poor stonecutter. Oh! How I wish I was a wealthy and powerful king with servants to serve me!"

As if by magic, his wish came true! Haku was suddenly the king, sitting in a royal carriage with silk curtains. After a while he began to feel the intense heat of the Sun. It became very hot in the carriage.

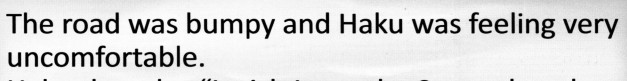

The road was bumpy and Haku was feeling very uncomfortable.

Haku thought, "I wish I was the Sun rather than the king. Then I would not have to suffer due to the heat or the bumpy road."

Magically, his wish came true again. He turned into the Sun and warmed up the Earth with his rays. After some time, the sky was covered with clouds. Haku the Sun tried to send his rays through the clouds but could not do so.

Haku was very unhappy, "I wish I was a rain cloud for it seems to have more power than the Sun." His wish was granted again and he changed into a huge rain cloud. He poured rain on the Earth. He directed rain on the stone he had been cutting. He was highly disappointed for he could not even move the stone.

Feeling sad, he thought, "As a rain cloud I cannot even move the stone. I had more power as a stonecutter. With my tools I could easily shape the stone any way that I wanted to. I shall be happy to be a stonecutter once again."

As he thought so, he turned back into a stonecutter. He was now a contented man. Happily, he went back to cutting the stone.

Moral: Be content with what you have.